Moonlight and Chocolate Trees

ANTHOLOGY 2

Compiled by
Elspeth Graham and **Mal Peet**

OXFORD
UNIVERSITY PRESS

Contents

Introduction

Sometimes, the title of a book is the hardest part to write. You want a title that sounds good, that will make people pick up the book and think 'I wonder what this is all about?' But you don't want a title that tells too much, that gives the game away, like *The Big Hairy Thing From Outer Space That Came Down And Ate The Next-door Neighbour's Lawnmower*.

A title for an anthology is a problem because there are so many different things in it. We decided to call it *Moonlight, Seas, and Chocolate Trees* partly because these words sound good together, but also because there is a lot of moonlight and seas on these pages, and also quite a bit about chocolate. (There's even a tube of Smarties in here somewhere.) There's also a water-buffalo and a leopard and a boy falling through the sky, and a recipe for butterscotch and a girl who turns into a giant blueberry. There's a granny who's a sumo wrestler and a dog that talks. This book will take you into the past and the future and into strange imaginary worlds. There are some very sad bits and some very funny bits. So you see the problem – what do you call a book that's got such a mixture of things in it?

You might as well call it *Moonlight, Seas, and Chocolate Trees*. We hope you enjoy it.

Mal Peet and Elspeth Graham

Street Child

BERLIE DOHERTY

This is London in the year 1865. Jim Jarvis' mum is too ill
to work, and she and Jim have been thrown out of their
home. They have been sent to live in the dreaded
workhouse.

The matron closed her ice-cold hand over his and
bent down towards him, her black bonnet crinkling.
Her teeth were as black and twisted as the railings in
the yard.

She pulled Jim along the corridor and into a huge
green room, where boys sat in silence, staring at
each other and at the bare walls. They all watched
Jim as he was led through the room and out into
another yard.

'Joseph!' the matron called, and a bent man shuffled
after her. His head hung below his shoulders like a
stumpy bird's. He helped her to strip off Jim's clothes
and to sluice him down with icy water from the pump.
Then Jim was pulled into rough, itchy clothes, and his
hair was tugged and jagged at with a blunt pair of
scissors until his scalp felt as if it had been torn into
pieces. He let it all happen to him. He was too
frightened to resist. All he wanted was to be with
his mother.

He was led back into a huge hall and told to join the queue of silent boys there. They stood with their heads bowed and with bowls in their hands. There were hundreds and hundreds of people in the room, all sitting at long tables, all eating in silence. The only sound was the scraping of the knives and forks and the noise of chewing and gulping. All the benches faced the same way. Mr Sissons stood on a raised box at the end of the room, watching everyone as they waited for their food.

Jim was given a ladle of broth and a corner of bread.

'I don't want anything,' he started to say, and was pushed along in the queue. He followed the boy in front of him and he sat on one of the benches. He glanced

round him, trying to catch someone's eye, but none of
the boys looked at him. They all ate with their heads
bowed down, staring into their bowls. The boy next to
him sneaked his hand across and grabbed Jim's bread.
Jim ate his broth in silence.

After the meal the man with the hanging head gave
Jim a blanket and showed him a room full of shelves
and long boxes where all the boys slept. He pointed to
the box Jim was to sleep in. Jim climbed into it and
found that he only just had enough room to turn over
in it, small though he was. He tied his boots to his
wrists in case anyone tried to steal them. The dormitory
door was locked, and they lay in darkness. ▪

Other stories by Berlie Doherty are on pages 40 and 82.
There is more about homelessness on pages 70 and 110.

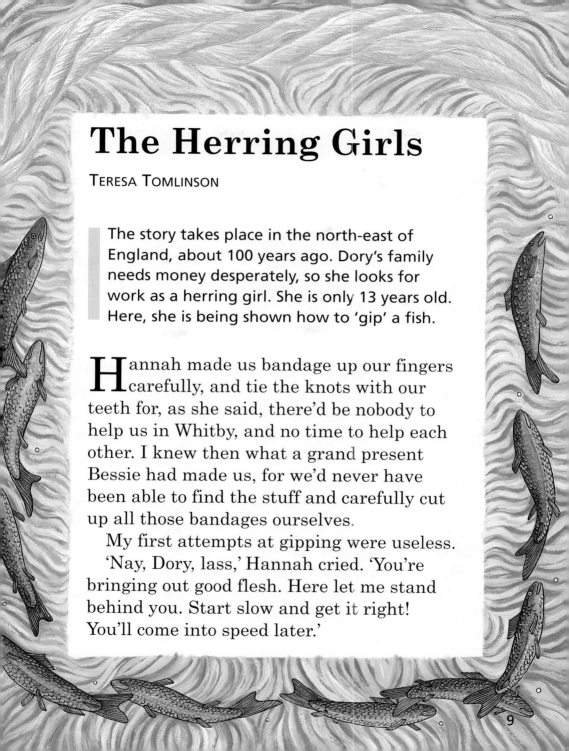

The Herring Girls

TERESA TOMLINSON

> The story takes place in the north-east of England, about 100 years ago. Dory's family needs money desperately, so she looks for work as a herring girl. She is only 13 years old. Here, she is being shown how to 'gip' a fish.

Hannah made us bandage up our fingers carefully, and tie the knots with our teeth for, as she said, there'd be nobody to help us in Whitby, and no time to help each other. I knew then what a grand present Bessie had made us, for we'd never have been able to find the stuff and carefully cut up all those bandages ourselves.

My first attempts at gipping were useless.

'Nay, Dory, lass,' Hannah cried. 'You're bringing out good flesh. Here let me stand behind you. Start slow and get it right! You'll come into speed later.'

I gripped the plump silver-skinned fish and Hannah put her hand over mine to guide the short sharp gipping knife.

'There now, make the cut in its throat like that, then push in so. Now a quick twist to pick up the guts, then gently flick — and out they come.'

The strong smelling herring guts slopped out onto the oilskin cover.

'Is that it?' I asked. The fish stared mournfully up at me, its eyes still bright on either side of its upturned nose. It looked almost untouched, just a small neat hole in its throat.

'That's it,' said Hannah. 'So long as the guts and the gills are out. Now try yourself.'

I copied her carefully, trying to judge the right spot to push in my knife, and just the right angle to pick up the guts when I twisted. And I did judge it right, but I pulled the knife out fast and a slimy spurt of fish guts shot up into my face. The stinking guts went up my nose, and into my mouth.

Hannah snorted with laughter and Mary Jane shrieked out loud. I staggered back, spluttering and spitting. The herring guts tasted foul.

'Ugh! Dory,' yelled Mary Jane.

'Eeeh! Dory love,' cried Hannah. 'I know it's wicked to laugh. But ... oh, your face! The guts should go in the gut tub, honey! There's a cloth behind you. Now then, come on, we'll try again.'

I wiped my face and shuddered, I couldn't stop spitting.

'It's all right you laughing,' I told Mary Jane. 'I've not seen you bring the guts out yet.'

We worked slowly all morning under Hannah's instruction, and when we'd used up almost thirty herrings, we'd begun to get the knack of hitting the right spot and bringing the guts out each time. Our arms and aprons were spattered with mess and our bandaged fingers slippery and wet, but Hannah had made us work slowly and we'd not cut ourselves.

Hannah set three baskets behind us and showed us how to judge the size of each herring, and throw the gutted fish carefully into the right basket. The smallest ones were called Matties. The medium-sized fish were called Mattiefulls, and the largest herrings were called Fulls. Hannah made us guess the size and shout it out as we gutted. If we guessed wrong, she scooped the fish out and made us do it all again. At noon she let us stop.

'I'll make us a pot of tea,' she said. 'Though there'll be no stopping for breaks in Whitby you know.'

Mary Jane slumped down onto a chair.

'Mind my decent furniture with those filthy oilies!' Hannah snapped. 'You can sit on the doorstep if you must.' ▧

There is more about child workers on pages 12, 22 and 84.

Pigeon Summer

ANN TURNBULL

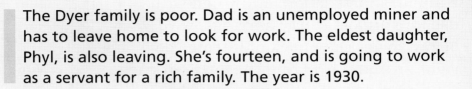

> The Dyer family is poor. Dad is an unemployed miner and has to leave home to look for work. The eldest daughter, Phyl, is also leaving. She's fourteen, and is going to work as a servant for a rich family. The year is 1930.

Mary wondered what it would be like at home without Dad or Phyl, just Mum and the little ones. She was always in trouble with Mum over one thing or another, but Phyl would cover up for her and defend her. She'd miss Phyl. And Dad. She'd enjoyed the time he had been off work; they'd spent a lot of it in the loft, looking after the pigeons.

Well, we've got a few more days all together, she thought.

But Saturday soon came. Phyl was up early, too nervous to eat breakfast. She pulled back her hair into a knot on the nape of her neck, and put on a dress of dark blue cotton with a white collar and pin-tucked front. Aunty Elsie, Dad's sister, had made her two dark blue dresses and two white aprons and had found her a hat with cherries on it and trimmed it with a blue ribbon.

Mary sniffed the new cotton of the dress. She was jealous. She'd never had a dress that wasn't an old one of Phyl's with the waist let out, or one of Aunty Elsie's cut down. And that hat! Phyl put it on, and was transformed into a grown-up.

Mary said, 'Oh, Phyl! Can I try it?'

She took the hat and darted into her parents' room to look at herself in the flecked mirror.

Mary's face was rounder than Phyl's, and her hair was a lighter brown and sprang about in curls. The hat hovered on top of them.

'It's too small,' said Mary. But the ribbon was silky, and the cherries trembled as she turned her head. She felt beautiful.

Phyl took it back and minced around the room. Mary put on a gentrified voice. 'Phyllis! Bring in the tea things!' They both giggled. 'Some chance!' said Phyl. 'I'll be scrubbing the passage, more like.'

At ten o'clock they were all at the bus stop in the square: Dad, Mary holding Lennie's hand, Mum carrying Doreen wrapped in a shawl, and Phyl holding a brown paper parcel of spare clothes and a purse with her bus fare in it. ■

 There is more about child workers on pages 9, 22 and 84.

An Angel for May

MELVIN BURGESS

> Tam is a very baffled boy. He was poking about in the
> ruins of an old farmhouse and somehow found his way
> through a hole in Time. Now he is 50 years in the past, at
> the time of the Second World War.

The town became less and less familiar as he got closer. No TV aerials on the roofs, old crock cars and horses on the roads. The cricket clubhouse was gone, and there were more allotments over the river where new houses had stood. The council estate on the other side of the main road was no longer there and Tam could see a couple of strange buildings, churches or chapels, rising above the rooftops. The fields around him had more flowers, longer grass. Even the air was different; it tasted of soot.

And then Tam stopped and stared because there on the hillside was a team of horses ploughing. Two stubby, powerful horses with their manes flicking in the wind, their strong necks forward and fat leather

halters around their shoulders. They toiled steadily around the hill with a man walking behind them, watching the plough share turn over the soil like a brown wave. A flock of crows followed them. The horses tossed their heads in the wind and pulled against the earth.

Tam felt like laughing again. He shook his head as if he could get rid of that image of the past and shake himself back to his own time, with big tractors and fields with short grass. But the horses strode around the hill, and the man held the plough handles with his strong arms and shouted at them; his voice came to Tam on the wind. He could even smell the horses. It was all real.

Tam knew where he was: Cawldale. But when? Mr Nutter had mentioned a war, but he had seen no signs of violence. First or Second? Suddenly Tam wasn't just afraid – he was curious. He ran on.

The bridge over the river was newer. Instead of tarmac there were stone slabs on it but underneath ducks still dabbed and quacked. They looked up at him out of one eye just as they used to – had, will – years later. They could have been the same ducks. ▪

Charlie and the Chocolate Factory

ROALD DAHL

> Greedy Violet Beauregarde is one of a group of children who have won a tour of Willie Wonka's amazing sweet factory. She grabs a stick of magic gum and begins to chew. She soon wishes she hadn't …

'Just so long as it's gum,' shouted Violet Beauregarde, 'just so long as it's a piece of gum and I can chew it, then *that's* for me!' And quickly she took her own world-record piece of chewing-gum out of her mouth and stuck it behind her left ear. 'Come on, Mr Wonka,' she said, 'hand over this magic gum of yours and we'll see if the thing works.'

'Now, Violet,' said Mrs Beauregarde, her mother; 'don't let's do anything silly, Violet.'

'I want the gum!' Violet said obstinately. 'What's so silly?'

'I would rather you didn't take it,' Mr Wonka told her gently. 'You see, I haven't got it *quite right* yet. There are still one or two things …'

'Oh, to blazes with that!' said Violet, and suddenly, before Mr Wonka could stop her, she shot out a fat hand and grabbed the stick of gum out of the little drawer and popped it into her mouth. At once, her huge, well-trained

jaws started chewing away on it like a pair of tongs.

'Don't!' said Mr Wonka.

'Fabulous!' shouted Violet. 'It's tomato soup! It's hot and creamy and delicious! I can feel it running down my throat!'

'Stop!' said Mr Wonka. 'The gum isn't ready yet! It's not right!'

'Of course it's right!' said Violet. 'It's working beautifully! Oh my, what lovely soup this is!'

'Spit it out!' said Mr Wonka.

'It's changing!' shouted Violet, chewing and grinning both at the same time. 'The second course is coming up! It's roast beef! It's tender and juicy! Oh boy, what a flavour! The baked potato is marvellous too! It's got a crispy skin and it's all filled with butter inside!'

'But how *in*-teresting, Violet,' said Mrs Beauregarde. 'You *are* a clever girl.'

'Keep chewing, baby!' said Mr Beauregarde. 'Keep right on chewing! This is a great day for the Beauregardes! Our little girl is the first person in the world to have a chewing-gum meal!'

Everybody was watching Violet Beauregarde as she stood there chewing this extraordinary gum. Little Charlie Bucket was staring at her absolutely spellbound, watching her huge rubbery lips as they pressed and unpressed with the chewing, and Grandpa Joe stood beside him, gaping at the girl. Mr Wonka was wringing his hands and saying, 'No, no, no, no, no! It isn't ready for eating! It isn't right! You mustn't do it!'

'Blueberry pie and cream!' shouted Violet. 'Here it comes! Oh my, it's perfect! It's beautiful! It's … it's exactly as though I'm swallowing it. It's as though I'm chewing and swallowing great big spoonfuls of the most marvellous blueberry pie in the world!'

There is more about sweets on pages 19, 36, 39, 50, 66, 68 and 104.

Charlie and the Chocolate Factory

ROALD DAHL, ADAPTED BY RICHARD GEORGE

VIOLET BEAUREGARDE: Just so long as it's gum, and I can chew it … then that's for me! *[She takes her own piece of gum out of her mouth and sticks it behind her left ear]* Come on, Mr Wonka, hand over this magic gum of yours … and we'll see if the thing works!

MRS BEAUREGARDE: Now, Violet … let's not do anything silly.

VIOLET BEAUREGARDE: I want the gum! What's so silly?

WILLY WONKA: I would rather you didn't take it. You see, I haven't got it quite right yet. There are still one or two things —

VIOLET BEAUREGARDE [Interrupting]: Oh, to heck with that! *[She grabs the gum and pops it into her mouth]*

WILLY WONKA: Don't!

VIOLET BEAUREGARDE: Fabulous! It's great!

WILLY WONKA: Spit it out!

19

MR BEAUREGARDE: Keep chewing, kiddo! Keep right on chewing, baby! This is a great day for the Beauregardes! Our little girl is the first person in the world to have a chewing-gum meal!

WILLY WONKA *[Wringing his hands]*: No – no – no – no – no! It isn't ready for eating! It isn't right! You mustn't do it!

MRS BEAUREGARDE: Good heavens, girl! What's happening to your nose? It's turning *blue*!

VIOLET BEAUREGARDE: Oh, be quiet, mother, and let me finish!

MRS BEAUREGARDE: Your cheeks! Your chin! Your whole face is turning *blue!* Mercy save us! The girl's going blue and purple all over! Violet, you're turning violet, Violet! What *is* happening to you? You're glowing all over! The whole room is glowing!

[Blue lights on only]

WILLY WONKA *[Sighing and shaking head sadly]*: I *told* you I hadn't got it quite right. It always goes wrong when we come to the dessert. It's the blueberry pie that does it. But I'll get it right one day, you wait and see!

MRS BEAUREGARDE: Violet …
you're swelling up!

[VIOLET begins backing off stage]

VIOLET BEAUREGARDE: I feel most peculiar!

[VIOLET now disappears off stage]

MRS BEAUREGARDE: You're swelling up!
You're blowing up like a balloon!

WILLY WONKA: Like a *blueberry!*

MRS BEAUREGARDE: Call a doctor!

MR SALT: Prick her with a pin!

MRS BEAUREGARDE *[Wringing her hands helplessly]*:
Save her!

WILLY WONKA: It always happens like this. All
the Oompa-Loompas that tried it finished up as
blueberries. It's *most* annoying. I just *can't*
understand it. ▪

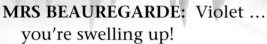

There is more about sweets on pages 16, 36, 39, 50, 66,
68 and 104.

Climbing in the Dark

NICK WARBURTON

It's Tess's first day as a maid in a big house. She's in the kitchen talking to the Housekeeper, Mrs Hutton.

There is a knock at the door and they both jump.

Mrs Hutton Oh no. Not him!

Tess Who is it?

There is another knock.

Mrs Hutton It's Mr Fry, the chimney sweep. And he can wait.

She takes a drink and ignores the next knock. Then she gets up slowly and opens the door. **Fry** *enters, looking cross and carrying some poles.*

Fry What kept you?

Mrs Hutton We're busy down here, Mr Fry.

Fry Busy? Huh! *(turning to call over his shoulder)* Don't stand there gawping, you little rat. Fetch in some of them poles.

Will, *Mr Fry's apprentice, comes in with some more poles. He is a small, crouching, frightened figure.*

Mrs Hutton	You've got a new boy, I see, Mr Fry.
Fry	A boy, Mrs Hutton? A rat on two legs more like. And an expensive one, too.

Will *puts the poles down and starts to cough.*

Fry	And you can cut that out, you maggot!
Mrs Hutton	Why, he's skinny as railings.
Fry	Of course he's skinny. He's got to get up chimneys, hasn't he? If he was plump he'd get stuck.
Tess	I think he needs a little water.
Fry	He needs a clip round the ear.
Mrs Hutton	*(Firmly)* Water, Mr Fry. You take your things through and I'll see to the boy.
Fry	But …
Mrs Hutton	Go on, Mr Fry. I'll bring him to you in two shakes.

Mr Fry *moves off, mumbling. Before he leaves, he turns.*

Fry	Don't pamper the little brat, that's all.

He goes out. **Will** *coughs again and* **Mrs Hutton** *helps him to sit down at the table.*

Mrs Hutton	You ought to be home in bed, my chicken.
Will	I ain't got no bed. I got a bit of straw on the floor.
Mrs Hutton	What's your name, boy?

Will	Will.
Mrs Hutton	Will what?
Will	Just Will. I don't know no other name. My father sold me to Mr Fry, to go up chimbleys.
Tess	Sold you? Your own father?
Will	Yes. 'E took me to Fry's 'ouse one day and then went 'ome without me. I found meself in this cellar full of brushes and things. Then I knowed. I was sold, to go up chimbleys.
Tess	But that's terrible.
Will	That's fathers for you, miss. They're all the same.

Mrs Hutton   Whatever must it be like, climbing about in chimneys?

Will   It's 'orrible, miss. The bricks stay so 'ot it 'urts, and the chimbley's dark and it twists about so you don't know where you are. And Mr Fry, 'e puts vinegar on me elbows and knees and stands me before the fire till I'm nearly roasted up.

Tess   But why does he do that?

Will   To 'arden the skin, miss. So I can grip on the chimbleys.

Mrs Hutton   Well, Will, there's some milk, and there's a spoon, and there's a pot of honey. You help yourself to that.

Will *eats ravenously.* **Mrs Hutton** *moves away from the table. She is upset.* **Tess** *joins her.*

Mrs Hutton   Poor little chap. Just look at him.

Tess   Is Mr Fry really so cruel? It's just not fair.

Mrs Hutton   That it isn't, Tess. Not fair at all. Now, you go up to the attic and set your things out. I'll look after Will.

Tess *goes off one way and* **Mrs Hutton** *gently leads Will off the other.*

There is more about child workers on pages 9, 12 and 84.

Alone in the Grange.

GREGORY HARRISON

Strange,
Strange,
Is the little old man
Who lives in the Grange.
Old,
Old;
And they say that he keeps
A box full of gold.
Bowed,
Bowed,
Is his thin little back
That once was so proud.
Soft,
Soft,
Are his steps as he climbs
The stairs to the loft.
Black,
Black,
Is the old shuttered house.
Does he sleep on a sack?

They say he does magic,
That he can cast spells,
That he prowls round the garden
Listening for bells;

That he watches for strangers,
Hates every soul,
And peers with his dark eye
Through the keyhole.

I wonder, I wonder,
As I lie in my bed,
Whether he sleeps with his hat on his head?
Is he really magician
With altar of stone,
Or a lonely old gentleman
Left on his own?

There is more about older people on pages 28, 30, 32 and 38.

You are Old, Father William

Lewis Carroll

'You are old, Father William,' the young man said,
'And your hair has become very white;
And yet you incessantly stand on your head –
Do you think, at your age, it is right?'

'In my youth,' Father William replied to his son,
'I feared it might injure the brain;
But, now that I'm perfectly sure I have none,
Why, I do it again and again.'

'You are old,' said the youth, 'as I mentioned before,
And have grown most uncommonly fat;
Yet you turned a back-somersault in at the door –
Pray, what is the reason for that?'

'In my youth,' said the sage, as he shook his grey locks,
'I kept all my limbs very supple
By the use of this ointment – one shilling the box –
Allow me to sell you a couple?'

'You are old,' said the youth, 'and your jaws are too weak
For anything tougher than suet;
Yet you finished the goose, with the bones and the beak –
Pray, how did you manage to do it?'

'In my youth,' said his father, 'I took to the law,
And argued each case with my wife;
And the muscular strength, which it gave to my jaw,
Has lasted the rest of my life.'

'You are old,' said the youth, 'one would hardly suppose
That your eye was as steady as ever;
Yet you balanced an eel on the end of your nose –
What made you so awfully clever?'

'I have answered three questions, and that is enough,'
Said his father. 'Don't give yourself airs!
Do you think I can listen all day to such stuff?
Be off, or I'll kick you downstairs!'

There is more about older people on pages 26, 30, 32 and 38.

My Granny is a Sumo Wrestler

GARETH OWEN

My granny is six foot three
My granny is built like a tree
My granny says – Nothing
I mean nothing
Frightens me.

When Granny walks down the streets
She scares every man she meets
Nobody gonna mess with her
My granny is a Sumo Wrestler.

My granny is six foot three
My granny she's built like a tree
My granny says – Nothing
I mean nothing
Frightens me.

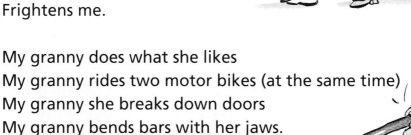

My granny does what she likes
My granny rides two motor bikes (at the same time)
My granny she breaks down doors
My granny bends bars with her jaws.

My granny she's six foot three (that's sitting down)
My granny she's built like a tree
My granny says – Nothing
Absolutely nothing
Frightens me.

My granny is a railway ganger
My granny is a wild head banger
My granny eats uncooked bison
My granny beat up Mike Tyson (in the first round).

My granny she's six foot three
My granny she's built like a tree (oak tree)
My granny says – Nothing
And I mean nothing
Ever
  Ever
    Ever
      Frightens me.

 There is more about older people on pages 26, 28, 32 and 38.

Granny Granny Please Comb my Hair

GRACE NICHOLS

Granny Granny please comb my hair
you always take your time
you always take such care

You put me on a cushion between your knees
you rub a little coconut oil
parting gentle as a breeze

Mummy Mummy
she's always in a hurry-hurry
rush
she pulls my hair
sometimes she tugs

But Granny
you have all the time
in the world
and when you're finished
you always turn my head and say
"Now who's a nice girl?"

 There is more about older people on pages 26, 28, 30 and 38.

So, will I get any Brownie points for saving Dad?

LIZZY 7 PUTS HER FIRST AID SKILLS TO USE
By Frank Corless

AMAZING Lizzy Burden aged seven saved her father's life by using skills she had learned at Brownies.

She kept a cool head after dad Bob, 61, collapsed in the bathroom with a heart attack.

Lizzy, whose Brownie pack had been given life saving lessons just two days before, rushed into action.

She said: 'I didn't panic. I just knew I had to help daddy.'

Lizzy immediately told mum Marie, 43, how to put him in the recovery position before dialling 999 for help.

She then dashed out in her nightie and slippers to get neighbour Maggie Parker who is a district nurse.

AWARD: Lizzy in her uniform

Maggie tried to resuscitate Bob before paramedics arrived.

The retired commercial manager was eventually revived in hospital and was yesterday recovering at home.

He said: 'Lizzy really was my little saviour. Without her I wouldn't be here.

'Amid all the chaos and panic she kept calm and saved my life. I am very proud of her and also very grateful.'

Mum Marie said: 'It is amazing how quickly children learn and understand. When Lizzy came home from Brownies two days before she said she had been told about the recovery position and practised

34

GRATEFUL: Bob with daughter Lizzy who helped save his life after he suffered a heart attack.

on me in the front room.

'This shows just how important organisations like the Brownies can be.'

Lizzy not only got Brownie points from her parents but has been awarded a prestigious commissioner's award.

Cath Rowland, division commissioner for the Guides Association, said: 'It was the first time I have applied for a commissioner's certificate – but it was well deserved. She did a wonderful job.'

She added: 'I read recently that Guiding was irrelevant in this day and age and I got so cross.

'It isn't irrelevant and this proves it.

'The Brownies do a first aid badge over a period of three years – and they don't forget what they have learned.'

Lizzy, of Wilmslow, Cheshire, had been working towards her first aid badge when her dad was taken ill.

She remembered being shown mouth to mouth resuscitation, the recovery position and how to call for an ambulance.

Shy Lizzy said yesterday: 'I didn't panic but I screamed out of the door first before I ran across to Maggie's.'

Paramedics yesterday praised the youngster for her 'incredible maturity'.

A spokesman for Cheshire ambulance service said: 'Lizzy's quick thinking saved her dad's life.

'It is always vital to get an unconscious person positioned correctly.

'It's incredible for a girl this age to have behaved so maturely.'

The *Guardian*, Saturday, August 21, 1999

The future's bright for the bean

Jill Treanor

Only Smarties have the answer to the origins of their name. Mystery continues to surround the identity of the person who had the smart idea to start manufacturing the brightly coloured, sugar-coated chocolates.

The Scots were the first to sample 'chocolate beans' in

1937. They liked them enough to persuade the makers to launch them nationwide the following year, calling them Smarties and packaging them in the tubes with the alphabet caps in which they are still sold.

Smarties are now Britain's most popular children's sweet.

Last year sales were valued at £49m, and are on track to match that again this year and remain £10m more than Milky Bar, their nearest rival. Nestlé, their owner, does not reveal the profitability of the little sweets. It is spending £3.5m supporting the brand this year.

The company is ploughing £1m alone into an advertising campaign next

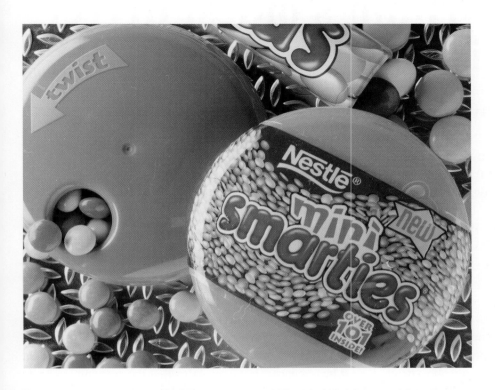

The colours now all taste the same, except for the orange ones.

month when the gang from the Smartie zoo will proclaim the launch of mini-Smarties. A third of the size of the originals, mini-Smarties are dispensed five at a time from a large plastic pod – Smartie-coloured and shaped, of course – which holds more than 100 sweets.

Sweeter than a conventional Smartie – there is more chocolate in relation to the sugar-coated shell – the mini-Smarties are crunchier, too, as it is possible to fit more of them in the mouth at one time.

 There is more about sweets on pages 16, 19, 39, 50, 66, 68 and 104.

The Times, 10th June, 1999

Britain's oldest driver is still cruising at 101

By Simon de Bruxelles

WHEN Millicent Buller taught herself to drive at the age of 14 most other traffic travelled on four legs.

Now, having recently celebrated her 101st birthday, Miss Buller is believed to be Britain's oldest driver.

Miss Buller still enjoys the six-mile drive from her home in Crediton, Devon, to Exeter for shopping. Once a week she drives to work as a volunteer steward at Exeter Cathedral.

She says that she developed her independent spirit as a youngster. "I taught myself to drive. I must have been 14 or 15. I had to pick up my father from work. Cars were a new thing to him and he never quite got the hang of them. I bought my first car, an Austin, for £25."

She worked as a Red Cross nurse in the 1920s and drove through blacked-out London streets during the Blitz. She has owned many cars but has few fond memories of her first: "The Austin was a terrible thing which broke down as soon as I got it and could never be trusted. My favourite was my Mini."

Today, she drives a Vauxhall Corsa but complains that the steering is a little heavy. "I used to drive everywhere but I shall probably give up in a moment. I don't seem to have the time. I see my car as a big pram. I go out, load it up with shopping and drive back."

The *Guinness Book of Records* said: "The country's oldest driver was Edward Newsome, from Brighton, who was still driving at his 105th birthday. But he died in 1997 and we do not have a record for the oldest living driver."

 There is more about older people on pages 26, 28, 30 and 32.

Butterscotch

FROM *ROALD DAHL'S REVOLTING RECIPES*

Makes approx 1¼ pt (3–4 mugs)

YOU WILL NEED:	1oz (25g) butter
large saucepan	*1oz (25g) castor sugar*
large jug	*1oz (25g) golden syrup*
whisk	*1pt (600ml) fat-free milk*
cling-film	*3fl oz (75ml) natural yoghurt*

1 In a saucepan, over a low heat, melt together the butter, sugar and golden syrup, stirring all the time until the sugar has dissolved (about 10 minutes). Add a little milk to the pan, then transfer to a jug.

2 Whisk in a little more milk, approx 2fl oz (50ml) followed by all the yoghurt.

3 Whisk in the remaining milk.

4 Cover with cling-film. Chill before serving.

 There is more about sweets on pages 16, 19, 36, 50, 66, 68 and 104.

Spellhorn

BERLIE DOHERTY

Spellhorn the unicorn and the Wild Ones are visitors from another world. They have found Laura, a human child, and they are taking her back to their world. Laura is blind; but when she is with the Wild Ones she can see again.

The colours around her dazzled and bewildered her. When she had first seen Spellhorn in her garden he had been silvery like the moonlight. Now he glowed red-gold with the fluttering light from the fire. When she looked round her she could see the eyes of the Wild Ones watching her, and they were like the burning nuts of wood in the flames, gleaming with sparks. Their faces shone in the yellow light, and some of them wore rich blood-red or earth-brown robes that had the lustre of the firelight in their folds, and their long hair drifted out like flames as they moved.

'Here, Girlchild.' Sloe crept over to her with a pot bowl cupped in his hands. 'Here's your bellyfill,' he said. 'Have it hot.'

Laura took the bowl gratefully, balancing it with the tips of both her thumbs and first fingers. It was very hot because it had been cooked in the flames of the big fire, and lifted out with stones.

'What is it?' she asked. The steam from it warmed her face.

'Mush,' said Sloe. 'And right good, too.'

When it was cool enough to eat Laura managed to sip at it. It seemed to be a kind of porridge made with oats and fruit; the taste reminded her a little of cherries and bananas and bread and honey and milk, and yet it wasn't really like any of these things.

But it was good, and warming, and the more she supped it the stronger she felt. She found herself lapping it up greedily, the way Water and Sloe were eating theirs, and licking out the bowl with her tongue. At last she put it down with a deep contented sigh, and saw them both cuffing each other with laughter.

'Right good bellyfill,' she said, and laughed with them.

Sloe scampered away with the bowl, and Water curled up by the fire to doze off. Laura looked round her. She was still confused by the brightness of everything, and by the startling colours of the sky and the trees. She held up her hands and spread them out wide. She clenched her fists and opened out her fingers again, slowly this time, one by one. She looked with wonder at the tiny lines on the palms of her hands and the fine hairs on the backs of her fingers, and the curved shiny shells of her nails. Then she pressed her hands against her eyes, letting the world go dark again. She tilted her head back and saw the red light of day filtering through the bars of her fingers, as if the sun was glowing inside her skin and bones. She laughed out loud and gazed round her again, smiling at the way the leaves fluttered like small green suns over her head. ▪

 Other stories by Berlie Doherty are on pages 6 and 82.

42

A HOLE IN THE HEAD

NICHOLAS FISK

This is the very beginning of a novel.

A Dog, Barking

In that grey-white wilderness, featureless and blank, there was nothing to see. Not even a horizon.

And, other than the hiss of wind-driven powder snow, nothing to hear. Nothing except –

The barking of a dog! Impossible! But listen… Somewhere, a dog was barking, barking, barking.

'Where is it?' Madi said, jerking her head from side to side. 'I can only hear it, I can't *see* anything!'

Jonjo wiped powder snow from his sister's vizor and said, 'Over there! It's got to be there! The MetrePak!'

Now she could just make it out: a MetrePak. A standard-issue metal cube exactly one metre square, standing all alone. The dull yellow of its walls was almost bleached white by clinging snow. The MetrePak seemed to come and go, vanish and reappear in the icy swirl.

And the dog kept barking, barking, barking.

'We've go to do something!' Madi said. 'Poor thing, it's tearing its throat to pieces!'

Jonjo stood still and said nothing. He was twelve, old enough to be cautious. Madi was two years younger, young enough to be reckless. She tugged at his arm.

'Please, Jonjo!' she said. *'Please!'*

Jonjo thought, Might as well do what she says. Can't just stand here. Stay still, and your face aches and your fingers stiffen. The cold cuts right into you…

'Come on!' she said, and trotted towards the MetrePak. She couldn't run properly, of course: not in all those layers of auto-heated clothes. He shambled after her. With each step, the snow hissed and whispered beneath their boots.

They reached the MetrePak. A curved wedge of snow sealed the lid, but it was not locked. Jonjo pushed his thickly-gloved fingers into the recessed handle and pulled. The lid came away. The MetrePak was open.

And there was the dog. Chained to a metal upright. It stopped barking – pulled at its chain, trying to reach them – and stood on its hind legs, scrabbling desperately.

'Good dog,' Madi said, moving forward. 'Nice dog.'

Jonjo held her back. 'Careful!' he said.

The dog frantically lunged at them. It twisted its head and gaped its mouth as if it were having a fit. Its collar strangled its throat. Its eyes rolled.

'Good boy,' Jonjo said. He kept his voice low and steady. 'What's your name, eh? Have you got a name?' Very slowly, he stretched out a hand protected by four thicknesses of fabric.

The dog seemed to have something stuck in its throat. It gasped, mouthed, swung its head. It gaped and showed sharp white teeth. Then, as if it were being sick, it brought up words.

The dog spoke.

'Good dog!' it said. 'Good dog good!' ▪

The Abradizil

ANDREW GIBSON

It all happened a very long time ago, in a very strange city, in a very distant land. The city was built on the banks of a river. When the morning sun was shining, it shone on hundreds of towers and spires and domes, and set them all sparkling with light. But the buildings beneath them were dark. The streets were narrow and small. The houses were crammed together, at crazy angles, in untidy rows. Their walls were peeling and crumbling, and their roofs sagged. They had lots of little rooms in them that bulged outwards, like bumps. It was a strange city, all right – a strange, bent, rather sinister city, and some strange, bent, rather sinister creatures lived there: magicians, wizards, goblins, dwarfs. The city was ruled by a sinister man, as well, whose name was Horg. You wouldn't have wanted to live in this city. But Franz lived there. ▪

Jack Black and the Ship of Thieves

CAROL HUGHES

It looks like it's all over for poor Jack. He is falling from the biggest airship ever built, and below him is an icy sea.

For the first few moments it seemed to Jack as though he wasn't falling at all. He felt as though he was hanging in the air, not moving, just hanging. Tiny details on the hull became crystal clear. He could see each criss-cross stitch and even the weave of the canvas. Nothing seemed real. His father stood at the window of the rear observation room, but he was not looking in Jack's direction.

'PAPA!' cried Jack, but as he cried, the world returned to its proper speed. The *Belle* shot up into the air and Jack plummeted towards the sea. His father had not heard him.

Once he was away from the shelter of the airship, the winds made light work of him. They threw him one way and he fell a hundred feet or so, then they snatched him up again and carried him away.

'I'm going to die,' he thought, as the

strong gusts blew his body about. 'Oh God, please let me fall quickly,' he prayed, but the winds wouldn't let him go. He spun through the air like a dry leaf on an autumn breeze, with his great coat swinging out about him. The winds blew him towards the storm that he had seen from the top of the airship. The swirling black clouds drew him in and the persistent thunder roared in his ears.

It was the strangest, darkest storm Jack had ever seen. The clouds were rank and sooty. The thick air seemed to scratch his eyes and he could hardly breathe. Violent flashes of fire exploded in the void beneath him and illuminated the blackness with an eerie orange light. Jack rolled over in the wind and the smoke. Enveloped in the thick dark clouds, he no longer had any sense of what was up or down. He didn't even seem to be falling anymore.

Suddenly there was a burst of fire far larger and brighter and closer than all the others had been and it sent Jack hurtling through the smoke. Within moments he was on the other side of the storm and out in the clear sky, falling with a scream towards the sea.

Behind him the thick clouds still churned and billowed, but now, as he turned over in the wind, Jack could see that this was no storm. The tower of smoke rose like the clouds of an erupting volcano from the funnels of an enormous warship. ▪

Harry Potter and the Philosopher's Stone

J. K. ROWLING

> The train that leaves from Platform Nine and Three Quarters at King's Cross Station goes to Hogwarts School of Wizardry and Witchcraft. On the train are two new boys. One of them, Ron, comes from an old wizarding family, so he already knows a bit about magic.

'What are these?' Harry asked Ron, holding up a pack of Chocolate Frogs. 'They're not *really* frogs, are they?' He was starting to feel that nothing would surprise him.

'No,' said Ron. 'But see what the card is, I'm missing Agrippa.'

'What?'

'Oh, of course, you wouldn't know – Chocolate Frogs have cards inside them, you know, to collect – famous witches and wizards. I've got about five hundred, but I haven't got Agrippa or Ptolemy.'

Harry unwrapped his Chocolate Frog and picked up the card. It showed a man's face. He wore half-moon glasses, had a long crooked nose and flowing silver hair, beard and moustache.

Underneath the picture was the name *Albus Dumbledore*.

'So *this* is Dumbledore!' said Harry.

'Don't tell me you'd never heard of Dumbledore!' said Ron. 'Can I have a frog? I might get Agrippa – thanks –'

Harry turned over his card and read:

Albus Dumbledore, currently headmaster of Hogwarts. Considered by many the greatest wizard of modern times, Dumbledore is particularly famous for his defeat of the dark wizard Grindelwald in 1945, for the discovery of the twelve uses of dragon's blood and his work on alchemy with his partner, Nicolas Flamel. Professor Dumbledore enjoys chamber music and tenpin bowling.

Harry turned the card back over and saw, to his astonishment, that Dumbledore's face had disappeared.

'He's gone!'

'Well, you can't expect him to hang around all day,' said Ron. 'He'll be back. No, I've got Morgana again and I've got about six of her ... do you want it? You can start collecting.'

Ron's eyes strayed to the pile of chocolate frogs waiting to be unwrapped.

'Help yourself,' said Harry. 'But in, you know, the Muggle world, people just stay put in photos.'

'Do they? What, they don't move at all?' Ron sounded amazed. '*Weird!*'

Harry stared as Dumbledore sidled back into the

picture on his card and gave him a small smile. Ron was more interested in eating the frogs than looking at the Famous Witches and Wizards cards, but Harry couldn't keep his eyes off them. Soon he had not only Dumbledore and Morgana, but Hengist of Woodcroft, Alberic Grunnion, Circe, Paracelsus and Merlin. He finally tore his eyes away from the druidess Cliodna, who was scratching her nose, to open a bag of Bertie Bott's Every Flavour Beans.

'You want to be careful with those,' Ron warned Harry. 'When they say every flavour, they *mean* every flavour – you know, you get all the ordinary ones like chocolate and peppermint and marmalade, but then you can get spinach and liver and tripe. George reckons he had a bogey-flavoured one once.'

Ron picked up a green bean, looked at it carefully and bit into a corner.

'Bleaaargh – see? Sprouts.'

They had a good time eating the Every Flavour Beans. Harry got toast, coconut, baked bean, strawberry, curry, grass, coffee, sardine and was even brave enough to nibble the end off a funny grey one Ron wouldn't touch, which turned out to be pepper.

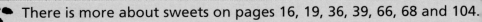

There is more about sweets on pages 16, 19, 36, 39, 66, 68 and 104.

Leopard Trail

(FROM THE SERIES 'WILD THINGS')

ELIZABETH LAIRD

> This story is set in Nairobi, a city in Kenya, in east Africa. A leopard has been prowling through gardens and eating people's pets. Tom Wilkinson has just realized that his pet cat has been shut out of the house.

He turned off his light and pulled the curtains back from the main window.

He saw the little black cat at once. She was crouching in a pool of moonlight on the lawn, tense, as if ready to spring, looking intently ahead. Tom had watched her doing that hundreds of times before. She must have seen some little creature, a beetle or a toad and, cat-like, she was stalking it.

Without stopping to think, he ran downstairs again and dashed through the sitting room to the verandah doors. Dad had locked and bolted them before he'd gone up to bed, but the bolts were oiled and the locks new. It was easy to undo them. Tom opened the door and stepped out onto the verandah.

His heart was thumping painfully in his chest. He'd never been outside so late at night before.

Nothing's different – it's only the garden, he told himself, but a consuming fear was touching him, something as ancient as man, a terror of the dark and its dangers, of teeth and claws and a swift, fearless enemy.

He hesitated. The verandah, surrounded by man-made walls and roofed with man-sawn timbers, felt somehow safe, but the lawn was no-man's land. He'd be easy meat out there.

Why am I making such a big deal out of this? he thought. The leopard's probably miles away.

Tiger, intent on her prey, hadn't turned her head. She looked so innocent, so homely and tame, playing at being a hunter, that Tom couldn't imagine that any harm could come to her. But as he watched, he saw in his mind's eye Bella in Tiger's place, Bella playing there on the lawn, absorbed in a toy, a frown of concentration on her baby face, oblivious to anything outside her safe, secure world. Tiger was just as clueless as Bella would be, faced with the cunning and hunger of a leopard.

He took a deep breath, stepped off the verandah and ran towards the cat. Then he heard it, a deep, throaty cough, a warning, a threat, and he turned round and saw the leopard.

He was crouching in the shade of a tree and Tom could see only half of him, only the outline of one side of his head, one round ear, one spotted cheek and one stern, unwinking eye that seemed to frown at him from under a heavy brow. ▪

 Other stories by Elizabeth Laird are on pages 55 and 80.

Elephant Thunder

(FROM THE SERIES 'WILD THINGS')

ELIZABETH LAIRD

> In this story, Tom Wilkinson has gone to Mount Kenya to see elephants. His guide, Titus Musau, has taken him to a pool where elephants like to wallow.

The first elephant, the big grandmother, had reached the water's edge. She dropped her trunk into it and swished it around for a moment, churning up the leaves of the water plants that were floating on the surface. Then, with a low growl of pleasure, she waded deep into the pool and sank down into the water, completely disappearing except for her trunk, which, black with muddy wetness, waved above the surface like a gigantic periscope.

One by one the others followed her. They dived and wallowed, rolled and splashed, sucking up water with their trunks and squirting it out again, lovingly nudging and caressing each other, slapping their wet ears against their heads.

Tom watched them, entranced. They were gentle, happy, relaxed, at ease with themselves. It was better than anything he could have imagined. He'd never seen anything like it. 'They're playing!' he breathed.

'Yes. They're just having fun.' Titus spoke quietly but above a whisper, knowing that the noise the elephants were making would cover his voice.

A little elephant calf, no more than a metre tall, hovered uncertainly on the edge of the pool, not daring to move in further than the shallow strip of water at the edge. She took a few steps into the water, missed her footing, and fell with a splash. She squealed indignantly and at once an older elephant, hovering nearby, pushed her upright with her leg, then sucked up a trunkful of water and squirted it all over her. It excited the baby and she began to run about at the edge of the pool, scattering a flock of wading birds

and charging with babyish fervour at a floating log.

Another elephant suddenly emerged from the trees at the edge of the clearing and stood watching for a moment before he ran into the water to join them. Titus raised the binoculars which he was carrying on a strap round his neck.

'It's the young bull who chased you yesterday,' he said gently. 'Look, you can see the wound on his face, beneath his ear.'

The young elephant, eager to get into the water, ran into the pool too hastily and knocked against a small female, hitting her with his strong muscular trunk. One of the biggest elephants, who had been slumped blissfully up to her shoulders in mud, rose with a sudden roar and faced him, her ears out at full stretch. The young male tossed his head up and down for a moment or two, then turned round and, his short tufted tail swinging, disappeared up the path.

Other stories by Elizabeth Laird are on pages 53 and 80.

Silver

WALTER DE LA MARE

Slowly, silently, now the moon
Walks the night in her silver shoon;
This way, and that, she peers, and sees
Silver fruit upon silver trees;
One by one the casements catch
Her beams beneath the silvery thatch;
Couched in his kennel, like a log,
With paws of silver sleeps the dog;
From their shadowy cote the white breasts peep
Of doves in a silver-feathered sleep;
A harvest mouse goes scampering by,
With silver claws, and silver eye;
And moveless fish in the water gleam,
By silver reeds in a silver stream.

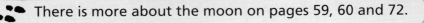

There is more about the moon on pages 59, 60 and 72.

Night Light

ANON.

There's no need to light a night-light
On a light night like tonight,
For a night-light's light's a slight light
When the moonlight's white and bright.

Moonlight

P. J. CHAUDHURY

I saw moonlight lying on the ground,
I stooped and touched the ground with my hand.
And found it was common earth,
Dust was in my palm.

 There is more about the moon on pages 58, 60 and 72.

Only the Moon

WONG MAY
TRANSLATED BY E. THUMBOO

When I was a child I thought
The new moon was a cradle
The full moon was granny's round face.

The new moon was a banana
The full moon was a big cake.

When I was a child
I never saw the moon
I only saw what I wanted to see.

And now I see the moon
It's the moon
Only the moon, and nothing but the moon.

There is more about the moon on pages 58, 59 and 72.

The Tide Rises, The Tide Falls

HENRY WADSWORTH LONGFELLOW

The tide rises, the tide falls,
The twilight darkens, the curlew calls;
Along the sea-sands damp and brown
The traveller hastens towards the town,
    And the tide rises, the tide falls.

Darkness settles on roofs and walls,
But the sea, the sea in darkness calls;
The little waves, with their soft, white hands,
Efface the footprints in the sands,
    And the tide rises, the tide falls.

The morning breaks; the steeds in their stalls
Stamp and neigh, as the hostler calls;
The day returns, but nevermore
Returns the traveller to the shore,
    And the tide rises, the tide falls.

 There is more about the sea on pages 62, 64, 72 and 82.

The Monster

JEAN KENWARD

I saw the great sea
      gnawing –
            gnawing at pebbles –
chewing the sand
    and spitting
        the wet sea-wrack.

I saw the great sea
    making
      his rolling patterns,
coming and going,
    rising
      and falling back.

I heard the great sea
    hissing as geese do;
  running
over my toes
    and ankles,
  cold as a knife,

I felt his sharp tongue
    creeping and crawling
  upwards –
knee high
  waist high ... then
    I ran for my life!

There is more about the sea on pages 61, 64, 72 and 82.

Until I Saw the Sea

LILIAN MOORE

Until I saw the sea
I did not know
that wind
could wrinkle water so.

I never knew
that sun
could splinter a whole sea of blue.

Nor
did I know before,
a sea breathes in and out
upon a shore.

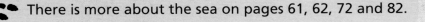 There is more about the sea on pages 61, 62, 72 and 82.

,

ROGER MCGOUGH

twould be nice to be
an apostrophe
floating
above an s
hovering
like a paper kite
in between the its
eavesdropping, tiptoeing
high above the thats
an inky comet
spiralling
the highest tossed
of hats

The Cocoa Tree:
the tree that gives us chocolate

Habitat

The cocoa tree is a tropical plant. It grows in places that are hot, wet and shady, close to the equator. The two main cocoa-growing areas of the world are the northern

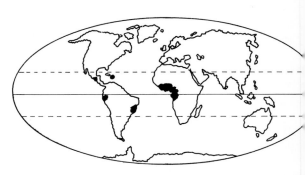

Cocoa-growing areas of the world.

part of South America and West Africa.

The cocoa tree.

Description

The cocoa tree is not tall. The average height of a full-grown tree is about seven metres. The main trunk is called the *chupon*. From the top of the chupon, branches grow out sideways. This part of the tree is called the *fan*. The leaves are glossy, green and broad. The cocoa tree produces a great many pink and white flowers, and what is unusual about them is that they grow from little 'cushions' on the trunk and main branches. A single cocoa tree produces hundreds of flowers every year, but only a few of these flowers produce a fruit, or *pod*.

Cultivation

Cocoa trees are difficult to grow. They need exactly the right combination of water and warmth. They need to be protected from wind and the direct heat of the sun, and for this reason young cocoa trees are often planted among larger, shade-giving trees. There are several deadly diseases which threaten the cocoa tree, and animals such as monkeys, rats and squirrels steal the pods for the sweet pulp they contain.

The cocoa pod

It takes about six months for the cocoa pod to grow to its full size and to ripen. Ripe cocoa pods are usually yellow or bright red, and they weigh about 450 grams. The shell, or *husk*, is tough and thick. Each pod contains thirty or more seeds covered in a sweet white pulp. These seeds are the *cocoa beans* from which ·chocolate is made. Cocoa pods do not split open by themselves. Wild trees need monkeys to do that for them and to scatter the seeds.

Heavenly stuff!
Every plant has a scientific name. The cocoa tree's is *Theobroma cacao*. The name *theobroma* comes from two Greek words meaning 'food of the gods'.

An opened cocoa pod.

There is more about chocolate and sweets on pages 16, 19, 36, 39, 50, 68 and 104.

67

How Cocoa is Grown

CADBURY LTD.

Cocoa and chocolate both come from the cocoa bean. The bean grows in pods on the cocoa tree, correctly named 'Theobroma cacao'. Cocoa trees are grown in places near the Equator, where the growing conditions are suitable. A steamy, damp climate is needed where there is plenty of rainfall and there are short dry seasons of three to four months. The Ivory Coast, Brazil, Ghana and Nigeria in West Africa, are all important producers but production is increasing in Malaysia too.

The cocoa tree looks rather like an apple tree but has broader, rich green leaves. The pods, unusually, grow straight out of the tree trunk and main branches. Each tree only has 20–30 pods a year. Inside each pod are 30–40 seeds enclosed in a sweet white pulp, rather like cotton wool. These are the cocoa beans. It takes a whole year's crop from one tree to make 454 grammes (1lb) of cocoa.

October to December is the main harvesting period in West Africa. The cocoa pods turn a rich golden colour when they are ripe. They are cut from the trees, split open, and the pulp and beans removed from the outside husk.

The cocoa beans are now piled up on a layer of banana tree leaves and more

leaves are put on top to cover them. They are left for five or six days for the beans to ferment. This is when much of the chocolate flavour develops. The pulp becomes liquid and drains away.

Later, the wet beans are dried in the sun and turned frequently to make sure they dry evenly. This process is important because any beans that are not dried properly could go mouldy when stored.

All the farmers take their produce to the buying stations where the beans are later weighed and packed into sacks.

There is more about chocolate and sweets on pages 16, 19, 36, 39, 50, 66 and 104.

What does Barnardo's do?

DIANNE CHURCH

In 1865 a young man called Thomas Barnardo visited London and was shocked to see thousands of children living on the streets. He was so angered by what he saw that he devoted his life to helping them. He opened homes so street children had somewhere warm and safe to stay. He started schools so poor children could learn to read and write. He provided training so they could get jobs and earn money. Barnardo's has worked with children for over 130 years.

◀ When Thomas Barnardo started the charity he cared for children in large homes. Today Barnardo's does its best to keep children with their families so they can solve their problems together.

Barnardo's helps nearly 30,000 children, young people and their families each year.

Barnardo's today

Today Barnardo's runs 250 local projects for children and families. Each project provides a different service. Some protect children who are in danger; and some find new mums and dads for children who can't live with their real parents.

Some projects provide playgrounds, libraries and quiet areas for children who live in poor areas and wouldn't otherwise have these things.

Barnardo's projects are all different because children and the help they need is so different. What they share though, is Thomas Barnardo's belief that every child has a right to a loving, secure childhood.

▲ *Thomas Barnardo helped 88,000 children during his lifetime. Because his homes and schools cost so much money to run, he spent a lot of his time giving speeches and writing letters to get people to give money.*

Barnardo's runs 250 projects across the UK.

 There is more about homelessness on pages 6 and 110.

The Restless Sea

Isobella Stanhope

Two-thirds of our planet, Earth, is covered by water. This water, our seas and oceans, is never still. Waves crash or ripple onto the land. Each day, the sea creeps up our beaches and then slips back again. These great movements of water are called *tides*. High tide is when the sea has crept up the beach as far as it can go; low tide is when the sea has slipped all the way down again. What causes these movements in our seas?

How are waves formed?

Huge waves can be formed by earthquakes or volcanoes under the sea. These are rare. The waves we see at the sea-side are built by the *wind*. A little breeze blowing on the surface of the sea makes little ripples called *catspaws*. A strong and steady wind can build **big** waves. As the wind blows over the surface of the sea, the water **begins** to roll. These rolling movements run through the sea, one after another, making the *crests* and *troughs* we call waves. When these rolling movements bump into a beach, the wave breaks and topples onto the shore. Some waves travel thousands of miles before they crash into land.

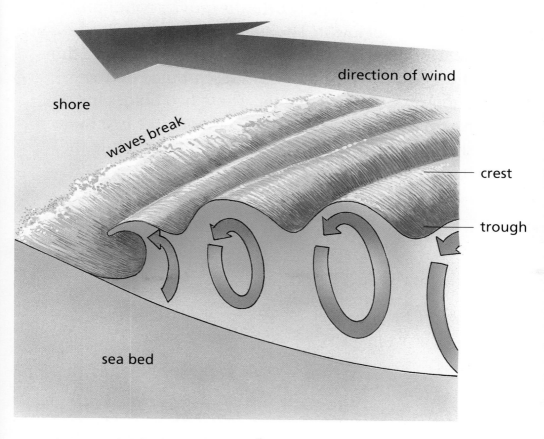

Fig 1 *How waves are formed.*

Why do the seas have tides?

Tides are caused by the sun and the moon. Both the sun and the moon have forces which pull on Earth, a bit like magnets. This force is called *gravitational pull*. The gravitational pull of the moon is stronger than the sun's because the moon is closer to us.

As the moon orbits Earth, its gravitational pull tugs at the seas below it. The seas on the side of Earth nearest the moon bulge towards it. At the same time, the spinning of Earth makes a sea-bulge on the opposite side of the planet. These two bulges move round the Earth following the moon, like two huge slow waves. The bulges cause high tides, while the troughs between cause low tides.

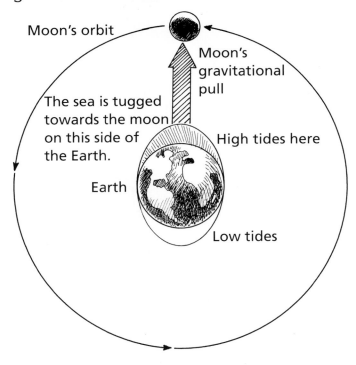

Fig 2 *How tides are formed.*

There is more about the sea on pages 61, 62, 64 and 82.
There is more about the moon on pages 58, 59 and 60.

The Camera Obscura

HUGH SCOTT

Oh! Feel sorry for Spindletrim as he runs from bullies in the playground.

Spindletrim Tom feels sorry for himself as his tiny legs race around children, and his ears hear William Cranston's feet beat the tarmac.

William Cranston is thick-limbed and tall as a man, and sparks leap when his feet beat, as he runs easily, after Spindletrim.

Spindletrim feels sorry for himself when fat Arnold Fetter rushes, forcing Spindletrim against a wall.

Arnold Fetter is as tall as a woman and smells of sweat even on the coldest day. His jacket is dribbled with food. His waistcoat (Arnold Fetter likes to borrow his father's waistcoat) is dribbled with food. And his shirt is dribbled with food. Spindletrim thinks Arnold Fetter's underwear is probably dribbled with food. And his skin.

Something like a stone hit Spindletrim's arm. When he snatched his arm away, something like another stone hit his ribs. But the stony things were fists, mean fists, full of bones, and attached to the fists were wrists, and all the rest of bony Robert Snarkey, who was the smallest of the three bullies, but quite the nastiest, because he practised being nasty. Spindletrim knew he practised because he saw Robert Snarkey every school day hurting children with his fists, kicking with his steel-tipped boots, cutting them – in a way – with horrid words; and he practised – everyone knew this – in a mirror in the cloakroom, finding worse ways to sneer, more terrible scowls; sniggering and laughing so his voice could follow you from one end of the street to the other; so he could bellow from the top deck of a tram-car...

As the fists struck Spindletrim's ribs; as Arnold Fetter's sticky palms banged on Spindletrim's ears; as William Cranston's fingers pulled his hair, and their three voices laughed and made stupid remarks, Spindletrim wished he could stay at home instead of coming to school.

School was a worrying place for Spindletrim. He worried about being late. He worried about being early and meeting the bullies. How terrible to be bullied at quarter to nine in the morning!

He worried in class about being bullied after class. Why was it important that the Battle of Britain was in 1066? That didn't help Spindletrim to get home faster; to dash from school when the bell rang, dodging through streams of pupils; running hard in High Street; stopping to pant behind the pillar box; racing along the pavements where shops sat bright and fat, into streets where lamp posts shone on their own feet and left little room between their iron bodies and house walls.

Then Spindletrim would thud downhill among taller and taller buildings, so that the sky got thinner between the gutters, and echoes whispered for ever; until he reached a lamp post that shared its glow with the antique shop that was home.

The shop was black with age. ANTIQUES in gold paint looked down from above the single window – or would have looked down, except that a burst gutter near the sky dropped water, wiping away the QU, staining a green line down the building, leaving the letters ANTI ES. So Spindletrim's home was called *Auntie's*, or to less imaginative people 'that junk shop in Steep Street'.

Suddenly.

In the playground, the bullies stopped bullying Spindletrim. William Cranston's thick arms barred the blows from Robert Snarkey and Arnold Fetter; and Spindletrim spent the rest of that school day worrying why William Cranston had grinned. ▪

 There is more about bullying on pages 78, 80 and 106.

Bad Girls

JACQUELINE WILSON

They were going to get me.

I saw them the moment I turned the corner. They were halfway down, waiting near the bus stop. Melanie, Sarah and Kim. Kim, the worst one of all.

I didn't know what to do. I took a step forward, my sandal sticking to the pavement.

They were nudging each other. They'd spotted me.

I couldn't see that far, even with my glasses, but I knew Kim would have that great big smile on her face.

I stood still. I looked over my shoulder. Perhaps I could run back to school? I'd hung around for ages already. Maybe they'd locked the playground gates? But perhaps one of the teachers would still be there? I could pretend I had a stomachache or something and then maybe I'd get a lift in their car?

'Look at Mandy! She's going to go rushing back to school. *Baby!*' Kim yelled.

She seemed to have her own magic glasses that let her see right inside my head. She didn't wear ordinary glasses, of course. Girls like Kim never wear glasses or braces on their teeth. They never get fat. They never have a silly haircut. They never wear stupid baby clothes.

If I ran back they'd only run after me. So I went on walking, even though my legs were wobbly. I was getting near enough to see them properly. Kim was smiling all right. They all were.

I tried to think what to do.

Daddy told me to try teasing her back. But you can't tease girls like Kim. There's nothing to tease her about.

Mum said just ignore them and then they'll get tired of teasing.

They hadn't got tired yet.

I was getting nearer and nearer. My sandals were still sticking. I was sticking, too. My dress stuck to my back. My forehead was wet under my fringe. ■

 There is more about bullying on pages 75, 80 and 106.

Secret Friends

Elizabeth Laird

She was the very first person I met on my very
first day at Dale Road Secondary School.
We bumped into each other at the door of
the hall where we'd been
sent to wait for our class
teachers.

'Oh, sorry,' she said.

'Me too,' I said.

She was much taller
than me, and quite
thin. She had a bush of
brown frizzy hair and
pale brown skin which
was dotted all over with
freckles. But what you
noticed straight away was
her ears. They were large,
and stuck out away from
her head. Like bats' ears.

'My name's Lucy,' I said.

'I'm Rafaella,' she said.

I don't know what got into me. Perhaps it was the
nervousness of starting a new school. Perhaps it was

the way she looked down at me, a little aloof, as if I was an interesting insect miles below her.

'I can't call you *that*,' I said, bursting into loud laughter. 'I'm going to call you Earwig. Eerie-Eerie-Earwig.'

She flushed up to the roots of her hair and turned away.

I could tell that tears had sprouted behind her eyelids, but she wasn't going to let me see them.

'Sorry,' I said awkwardly. 'Rafaella's a nice name actually. Sort of unusual, but so what?'

It was too late. Other people, standing silently near by, not yet knowing how to talk to each other, had overheard us.

I saw one boy nudge another and look up at Rafaella's closed pale face.

'Earwig,' he whispered, and they both giggled.

I've often thought I could have stopped it then and there, stood up for her, got things back on to the right track, but I didn't. I just waited, standing and fiddling with the pleats of my new navy uniform skirt, letting the laughs and the sideways glances go on round the hall.

I'm going to regret that moment till the day I die. ▪

There is more about bullying on pages 75, 78 and 106. Other stories by Elizabeth Laird are on pages 53 and 55.

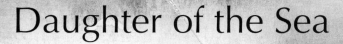

Daughter of the Sea

BERLIE DOHERTY

My tale is of the sea. It takes place in the far north, where ice has broken land into jagged rocks, and where black and fierce tides wash the shores. Hail is flung far on lashing winds, and winters are long and dark. Men haunt the sea, and the sea gives up to them a glittering harvest. And it is said that the people of the sea haunt the land.

My tale is of the daughter of the sea. The best way to hear the tale is to creep into the lee of the rocks when the herring boats have just landed. The gulls will be keening around you. The women hone knives on the stones, and their hands will be brown from the wind and the fish-gut slime. And as they work they talk to each other of things they've always known.

That's when the story's told.

Imagine a woman called Jannet, standing on the weed-wet stones. It would be dark, and the spray would be scraping her cheeks and the wind would be delving into her hair. She would be looking into the damsony dark and seeing nothing. And imagine her husband, Munroe Jaffray, crouching into his boat with the wild waves lumbering round him. And there's another to think of. Eilean o da Freya. Some say she's as weak in the head as a stunned herring. Others say she has the wisdom of the ancients. Jannet, Munroe, and Eilean. They're the ones who know for sure what happened on the night of the freak storm.

This is the tale. ▪

There are more stories by Berlie Doherty on pages 6 and 40.
There is more about the sea on pages 61, 62, 64 and 72.

Premlata and the Festival of Lights

RUMER GODDEN

> This story takes place in India. Mamoni's husband has died, and life is hard for her and the children – Premlata and her brother Ravi. But they do have Dhala to help them.

Dhala was their beloved water-buffalo. She was called Dhala, meaning 'fair', because although she was dark grey she had a small white spot on her forehead. Dhala was big enough for Ravi to ride on her back; she had long curved-back horns, her nose was soft and broad while her eyes were dark and kind and had lovely long lashes. She lived in a lean-to shanty at the back of the hut and was part of the family. Through all their troubles Mamoni had kept Dhala. 'Kept!' said Mamoni. 'She keeps us.'

Dhala gave them milk, enough for all of them and for Mamoni to make the curd and soft cheese she sold to Paru Didi. Sometimes a farmer would hire Dhala to plough or to pull a cart but Mamoni was careful of that: a driver could be cruel and twist a buffalo's tail or let the heavy wooden yoke rub her neck raw. Dhala even gave them her dung: if

she dropped any while she grazed, Ravi would gather it up carefully in a basket and bring it home where Mamoni would take a lump and plaster it on the hut's outside wall, pressing it flat with her open hand so that each pat had her fingerprints. When the dung had dried it made good slow-burning fuel for the stove.

Every day, all day, Ravi took Dhala to graze on the plain. How else could they have fed her? Because she was a water-buffalo, he had to take her first to the field water-hole where she sank with only her nose showing and the tip of her horns, which was buffalo bliss. In the evening he brought her home – 'cowdust time', the villages called it, because the cattle, treading the clay paths, raised the dust. Then she had to be milked, given a pail of water and some hay and husks for the night.

Ravi was ten, a dark handsome boy, but he was angry and bitter – because it seemed that nobody cared. 'I should be at school,' he said to Prem – never to Mamoni.

Prem knew he did not mean the village school but the big one at Pasanghar where he had been top boy of

his class. 'I would walk the three miles there and back if only I could go.' How much nicer, Prem thought, not to go to school, sitting, chanting lessons, having drill, being ordered about, instead to be out on the plain with Dhala, dreaming under a blue sky, but, 'I need to be at school,' mourned Ravi. 'Soon I'll forget how to read.'

There had been a day when, coming home early, he had met Mamoni going out. She was carrying their hand-lantern and tried to hide it in her sari, so that Ravi knew at once she was taking it to sell to the money-lender. 'You can't do that,' he had said.

'Son, I have to. We have the little oil lamp...' But Ravi had taken the lantern and put it back on its hook.

'I am going to the money-lender,' he said. 'I am the man of the house now', and he had gone to the shelf where he kept his books, the few that had been saved.

'No! No!' Mamoni cried. 'You can't do that. You'll need these books some day.'

'What day?' Ravi had asked in scorn. 'We need the lantern now.' He tied the precious books into a bundle and went out.

Now he really might forget how to read, and at supper that evening Prem put out a hand to pat him. He shrugged her off. 'Stop that! I'm just a buffalo boy, I tell you.' But later that night she had found him in Dhala's stall, his face pressed against the big hairy neck and he was weeping. She had gone away on tiptoe. ▪

There is more about child workers on pages 9, 12 and 22.

No Gun for Asmir

CHRISTOBEL MATTINGLEY

Asmir comes from Bosnia Herzegovina. That name
twists the tongues of people who do not know it. But
Asmir was born in Sarajevo. And it rolls off his tongue
like the smooth creamy sauce and the tender meat of
his grandmother's *musaka*.

Asmir remembers how the mountains rose sparkling
with snow in the winter all round Sarajevo. And in the
summer the trees swept like green waves up the
slopes. The domed roofs of the mosques gleamed like

moons among the houses and the minarets spiked the skyline. Morning, noon and evening the *muezzins'* call to prayer used to echo out across the city.

Asmir's father, Muris, was a lawyer in Sarajevo. Asmir's mother, Mirsada, was a chemical engineer in a chocolate factory. Asmir's brother Eldar was still only a baby, just twelve months old.

But Asmir had many other playmates. They used to meet every day in the park near their homes, running among the trees, chasing, hiding, swinging, see-sawing, rolling on the grass, calling, laughing.

Until one day, war came to Sarajevo. Hundreds of soldiers arrived, firing rifles, firing guns. Tanks rumbled through the streets. Aircraft flew over the city dropping bombs.

The smell of burning made Asmir's stomach sick. The smoke made his eyes sting. The sight of his friend the postman lying on the street with all the letters spilling out of his bag made his heart shudder. It was too late to help the postman.

Asmir gathered up the bloodstained letters. But when he took them to some of the addresses, the houses were burning heaps or hollow holes. He ran

home clutching the crumpled envelopes. His grandmother washed his hands and cooked him *ustipci*. They were his very favourite. But that day he could not swallow. The pancakes stuck in his throat.

Morning and night the tanks rumbled and the rockets exploded. Midday the sky filled with droning planes and the crack of snipers' rifles. There was no electricity to amplify the *muezzins'* call. It seemed to Asmir as if the soldiers had bombed God.

Then they bombed the chocolate factory. The smell of the chocolate choked Asmir to the bottom of his lungs and made his stomach churn. The chocolate burned but his mother came home. Asmir hugged her tight, and that night he crept into bed between her and his father. And the bad dreams went away.

First Haiku of Spring

ROGER MCGOUGH

cuck oo cuck oo cuck
oo cuck oo cuck oo cuck oo
cuck oo cuck oo cuck

Haiku

KOBAYASHI ISSA (JAPANESE)

The snow is thawing;
suddenly, the whole village
is full of children!

Hummingbird

X. J. KENNEDY

Cried a scientist watching this creature dart by,
'Why its wings are too small for it! How dare it fly?'

So he figured and figured and finally found
That it just couldn't possibly get off the ground,

And they made him Professor. But still, hummingbird
Kept on flying to flowerbeds. It hadn't heard.

Rain

GEORGE MACBETH

wh
en
t
he
r
ai
n
is
f
al
li
ng
i
n
lo
ng
c
ol
um
ns

we
ar
e
in
cl
in
ed
t
o
fo
rg
et
w
ha
t
a
mi
ra
cl
e
it
i
s.

The Electronic House

WES MAGEE

cooker. blanket.
toothbrush. fire.
iron. light bulb.
tv. drier.
fridge. radio.
robot. drill.
crimper. speaker.
kettle. grill.
slicer. grinder.
meters. fan.
slide-projector.
deep-fry pan.
vacuum cleaner.
fuses. shocks.
freezer. shaver.
junction box.

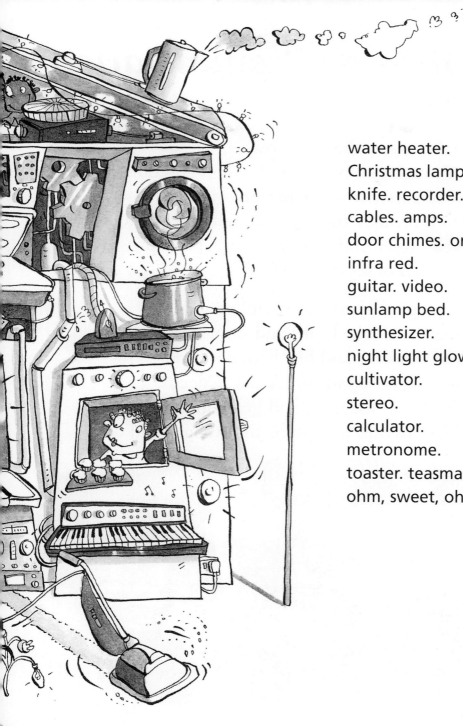

water heater.
Christmas lamps.
knife. recorder.
cables. amps.
door chimes. organ.
infra red.
guitar. video.
sunlamp bed.
synthesizer.
night light glow.
cultivator.
stereo.
calculator.
metronome.
toaster. teasmade!
ohm, sweet, ohm.

Hints on Pronunciation

ANON.

I take it you already know
Of tough and bough and cough and dough?
Others may stumble but not you,
On hiccough, thorough, lough and through?
Well done! And now you wish, perhaps,
To learn of less familiar traps?

Beware of heard, a dreadful word
That looks like beard and sounds like bird,
And dead: it's said like bed, not bead –
For goodness sake don't call it 'deed'!
Watch out for meat and great and threat
(They rhyme with suite and straight and debt.)

Crocodile Alphabet

ANON.

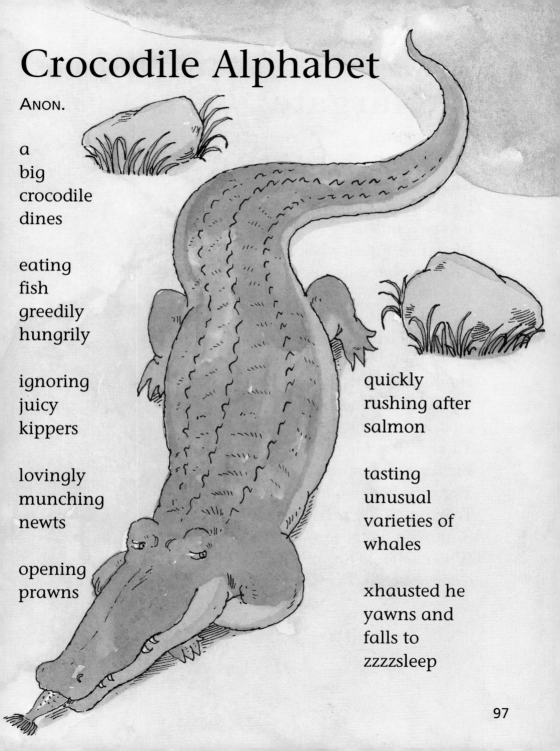

a
big
crocodile
dines

eating
fish
greedily
hungrily

ignoring
juicy
kippers

lovingly
munching
newts

opening
prawns

quickly
rushing after
salmon

tasting
unusual
varieties of
whales

xhausted he
yawns and
falls to
zzzzsleep

The Last Steam Train to Margate

JOHN HILL

Gossssh
I wisssh
I were a busss
It's muccch less work
And muccch less fuss
I Sssshould like that
I Sssschould like that
I SSSSSCHOULD like that
I Sssshould like that
De-deedle-dee
De-diddle-dum
Just look at me
'Cause here I come
Faster and faster
Tickerty-boo, what'll I do?
Tearing along, terribly fast
Singing a song, sounding a blast
Whoo, whoo! Out of the way
Goodness me, I can't delay!

You can relax, I have to run
Follow the tracks into the sun
Pain in my back, aches in my joints
Tickerty-tack, here are the points
Diddly-dee, diddly-dee
Diddly WIDDLY diddly dee!
Far to go? Not very far.
Little black tunnel
(Tickerty WHAAAH!)
Look over there. What can it be?
Lucky old you, clever old me
Come all this way, never go wrong
Come every day, singing a song
Down to the seaside. Let's have a cheer.
Oh, what a train-ride. We're nearly there,
We're nearly there, we're nearly there, we're nearly there.
And now I'd better slow right down
In half a mile we reach the town
And then you take your buckets and spades
And dig the sand and watch the parades
And sing and paddle and splash in the sea
And have ice cream and jelly for tea
And Coca Cola, orange squasssssh
And ginger beer, hooray we're here
But gosssh I'm tired
Oh gosssh I'm tired
Oh gosssh I'm tired
Hohhh
GOSSSSSSSSSSSSSSSHHHHHHHHHHHHHH

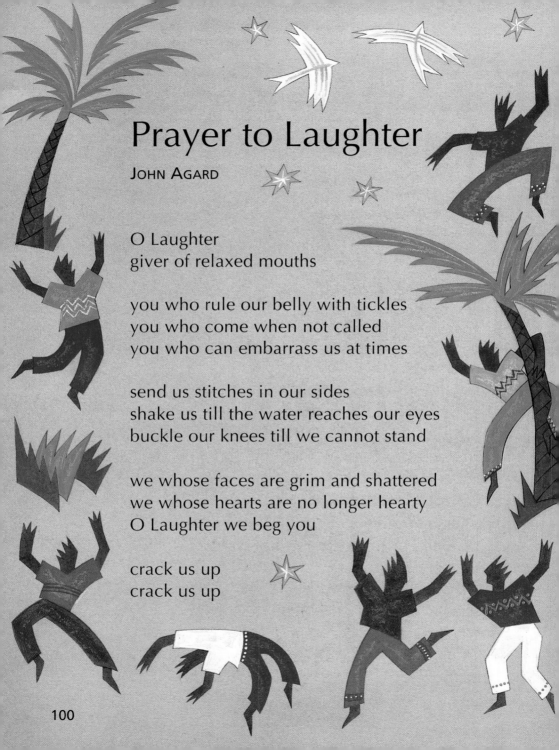

Prayer to Laughter

John Agard

O Laughter
giver of relaxed mouths

you who rule our belly with tickles
you who come when not called
you who can embarrass us at times

send us stitches in our sides
shake us till the water reaches our eyes
buckle our knees till we cannot stand

we whose faces are grim and shattered
we whose hearts are no longer hearty
O Laughter we beg you

crack us up
crack us up

Benediction

JAMES BERRY

Thanks to the ear
that someone may hear

Thanks to seeing
that someone may see

Thanks to feeling
that someone may feel

Thanks to touch
that one may be touched

Thanks to flowering of white moon
and spreading shawl of black night
holding villages and cities together

What's so amazing about giving blood?

When you give blood, you'll be doing one of the most amazing things anybody could dream of – saving a life.

You can enable someone to receive a desperately needed transfusion. Some operations, for instance, require literally pints and pints of blood. Or just as importantly, components extracted from your blood, such as plasma, can play a key role in a range of procedures such as treating burns or preventing infection.

As new treatments are developed and more operations carried out, hospitals throughout the country need more and more blood, all year round.

Seven year old Lamech has had to have more than 20 operations in two years to treat a rare kidney disorder, and owes his life to blood donors.

For example, in England and North Wales alone, nearly two and a half million donations are needed each year to help the NHS save lives.

But, only 5% of the UK population currently give blood.

It's *all* types of blood we need – not just rare ones. In fact, the commoner the blood type, the more we need.

So even if your blood is one of the most common types – group O, for example – you can be sure that by donating regularly, two or three times a year, you really *are* doing something amazing.

When Debra became pregnant, complications set in. Treatment with blood components played a vital part in making sure she gave birth to a healthy baby girl.

Do something amazing today

Save a life

Give blood

Advertisements

◀ Jammie Dodger Dipz!

Now instore – New Jammie Dodger Dipz! Delicious shortcake fingers with yummy jam! Great fun to eat on the move or as a treat! Available in single or triple packs. Watch out for new Jammie Dodgers coming very soon - fantastic for lunchboxes!

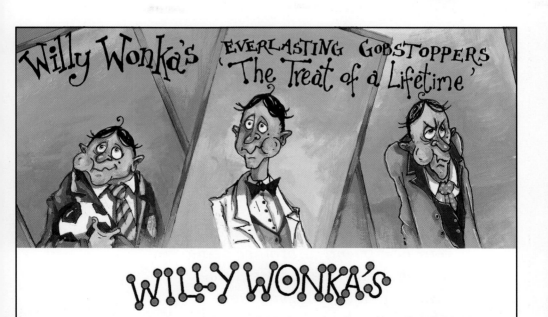

There is more about sweets on pages 16, 19, 36, 39, 50, 66 and 68.

Boys Behaving Badly

JEREMY DALDRY

It can be for any reason
– but whatever reason it is, there is
absolutely no excuse

for being a bully.

Bullying is based on ignorance and fear, it's based on stupidity and prejudice and it's based on the 'that person is different from me and my mates, he must be weird,' syndrome.

So how do you stop yourself from becoming a bully?

There is one very simple way.

Next time you and your mates are teasing someone, calling them names or just generally making their life less than pleasant – **just stop**.

Stop and think how you would like it, if it was *you or your best friend* or *brother* being picked on, being made to feel like you didn't belong, like you were a bit of a freak. *Just stop and think* how isolated and scared you might feel, how alone and desperate.

Stop bullying someone, stop making their life hell and give them back their self respect. You had no right to have taken it away from them in the first place.

Bullying time out.

Here's a question.

What's the difference between bullying someone and teasing them or taking the mickey?

Answer: Absolutely nothing if every time you see someone you tease them or take the mickey out of them.

No one minds being **ribbed** or being the **butt** of a joke from time to time but if you are always making someone the **punch line** of a gag, you are

bullying them.

It's a funny old thing but sometimes bullies **don't realise** they are bullying someone – they usually just think they are **having a laugh** and the only reason that their victim is getting upset is because they haven't got a **sense of humour**.

AND THAT IS SO WRONG.

 There is more about bullying on pages 75, 78 and 80.

Country Watch

DICK KING-SMITH

For hundreds of years fox-hunting with all its pageantry has been a part of the English country scene, and part of English poetry and story, painting and song. Despite all that, I happen to think that it should be stopped, for the simplest of reasons. It's not fair to the fox.

To begin with, I don't believe that he does all that much damage. If you forget to shut your chickens up at night, more fool you. He'll kill them. He'll probably kill them all, because instinctively as long as something flutters in front of him, he'll snap at it. And of course the fox will sometimes take poultry by day.

The duck that's waddled too far from the pond, and broody hen that's chosen to make a nest in the hedge-bottom, the cockerels that have ranged too far – all are fair game.

One April day a fox killed sixteen of my cockerels in a few moments, and when I got up to milk the following morning, and pulled back the curtains and looked out of the bedroom window, there he was, sitting on the lawn below beside the sundial, looking up at me, ears cocked. His red coat shone, his front paws were neatly together, his white-tipped brush was curled round him.

I dressed quickly and ran downstairs for my gun. I didn't know if this was the cockerel-killer or not, but I didn't care. He was going to pay for the massacre.

When I peeped over the garden wall, there was no sign of the fox. Well, that's not quite true – there was one. Fox-droppings are called 'scats'. He had left a present for me, a nice steaming pile of them on the steps of the sundial. Yes, I would have shot him, but still I don't think that anything a fox does ought to condemn him to a long terrifying chase and an exhausted bitter death in the jaws of a pack of hounds. ■

A Home to go to

KATE HAYCOCK

The word 'home' can mean different things to different people. For this person, home is a couple of benches in a park. Tomorrow, home could be a different couple of benches, a shop doorway or a bus shelter.

In every country in the world, and for many different reasons, there are people living on the streets, sleeping out in the open. They are out in all weathers, when most of us are safe and warm at home. They are homeless.

Homelessness does not mean simply sleeping rough or living on the streets. Having a home is more than having a roof over your head and being protected from the elements (rain, snow, etc). A home is something that belongs to you. You may not own it, but it is a place where you feel at home; a place where you are in control. It is yours; a place where you are entitled to be. A home is not just a place to sleep, it's a place to live.

Home is somewhere where we should be able to make plans, entertain friends, relax, spend time with our families and do our homework. For most of us it's the place we go back to after we've been shopping, working, attending school or college. Usually, our homes have kitchens where we can cook meals, bathrooms with running water, and electricity and heating.

Most of us could not imagine life without these 'basic essentials'. A home is something we take for granted. When we have a friend who is always out, we joke, 'Haven't you got a home to go to?' But for many people it's not a joke. They do not have homes. These people are not just somewhere else in the world, in poorer countries. They're not even just somewhere else in our own country; they may be only a few streets away. Why do we have homes when they do not?

The most visible signs of homelessness are the people who live and sleep on the streets of our cities, or in tents in our public parks. They have literally nowhere else to go. But there are also people who may have somewhere to sleep tonight, but who have no idea where they will sleep tomorrow night, or the night after that. Although they are homeless, they are much less visible than people sleeping on the streets because they disappear at night. Where do they go? Some find shelter in hostels run either by local authorities or by charities, which provide beds for a night and some hot food.

There is more about homelessness on pages 6 and 70.

Thematic Links